THEIR FINEST HOUR

Radar
and the
Secret Wireless War

Mark T. Jones with John G. Bentley

RAVETTE PUBLISHING

First published in 2010

by Ravette Publishing Limited
PO Box 876
Horsham
West Sussex RH12 9GH

ISBN: 978-1-84161-343-7

Information contained in this book is to the best of our knowledge accurate and complete
from the sources researched at the time of going to print.

Dedicated to those men and women
who gave so much
that we might be free to think for ourselves.

With particular thanks to
my friend and colleague Professor P. R. Banerjee,
and to Mr Stanley Abercrombie
and Mr Raymond Fautley
for their valuable insights.

Mark T. Jones

Contents:

Radar
and the
Secret Wireless War

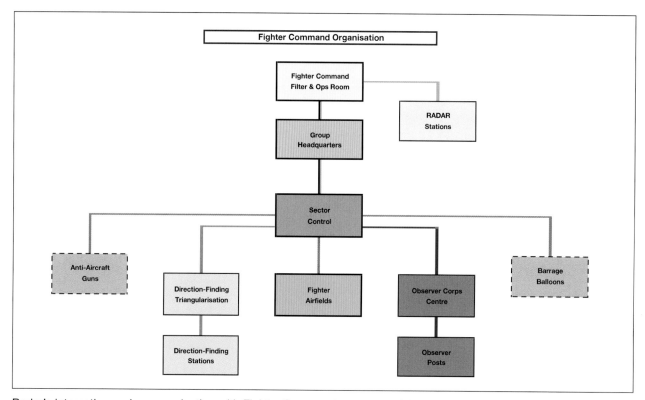

Radar's interaction and communication with Fighter Command was essential in directing the RAF fighters to the location of incoming bombers and raiders

Introduction

Throughout history, war has been an engine of change.

Empires and kingdoms have been toppled, great cities destroyed and nations brought low. Whether an aggressor nation or one trying to resist aggression, it has always been essential to engage in cunning deception and strategies to outwit the enemy.

In the quest to survive, countries have been quick to use resources to develop new means of defence and attack, hence the old adage about necessity being the mother of invention.

The Second World War (1939-1945) was to see all the key belligerents employ skills and guile to develop weapons and devices that might just give them the edge over their enemy.

A key weapon in their armoury was deception. All sides sought to gather information and to use it to gain advantage and this saw the warring nations making use of the very finest minds to outwit their enemies. In the titanic struggle for survival, mankind was to see its skills employed to develop new weapons, surveillance techniques, and strategies to gain advantage. Science and mathematics were to be employed to crack codes and deceive the enemy. Many of those involved in such work are still shrouded in secrecy and the work of other remarkable individuals or of daring deeds has only recently come to light.

The world as we know it today has been shaped by the events of World War Two. Radar and similar devices continue to shape our daily lives and as for surveillance, well some say we live in a Big Brother society.

What follows will shed light on a momentous historical period. The past as always, has something to teach us about our present world. Maybe it will also help us to ask searching questions about the society we live in.

New century, new horrors

As a new century dawned, dangers and threats seemed ever present, some internal, some external. New technologies opened up a wealth of possibilities for individuals and governments seeking to destabilise and destroy.

The optimism and hope that greeted the arrival of the Twentieth Century soon evaporated as fresh conflicts and wars broke out. The assassination of Archduke Franz Ferdinand, heir to the Habsburg throne, soon became the *casus belli* (Latin for 'cause for war') for what escalated into the war we know of as the First World War (1914-1918). This first, truly global conflict saw science put to use as never before. Networks of spies and secret agents were employed to gather information on the enemy – the most famous of these being a woman spy called Mata Hari (she was executed in 1917 by firing squad for spying). Codes and ciphers were standard. More and more deadly weapons were developed, including the tank (a British invention which acquired its name from its code name – water tank) and chemical warfare (gas warfare using chlorine and mustard gas). Machine guns decimated entire armies, whilst mortars were perfected so that they were even more lethal. A new form of warfare - aerial warfare came into its own. Airships (sometimes known as dirigibles or Zeppelins) were able to launch daring bombing raids on Britain, whilst aircraft played a key role in reconnaissance and showed that they had the potential to cause serious damage. Germany and her allies may have capitulated in 1918, but it was clear that all sides had paid a heavy price, the only winner being war itself in adding to its gory tally of victims. The carnage and horror of the First World War demonstrated just how industrialised war had become.

A recruit poster circa 1915 featuring one of the dreaded Zeppelins over London

The blame game

With the end of the First World War came the quest for spoils, the desire to blame and a sense of weariness.

As the guns fell silent with the Armistice, Europe and to some extent the world lay battered and bruised. Millions had died, thousands had been wounded, Empires and monarchies had fallen and revolution was in the air. Mankind's ability to wreak havoc upon the world was there for all to see, not just in the battlefields of Flanders, but far and wide. From the Turkish genocide of the Armenians (still routinely denied by the Turkish state) to the terror that followed the Russian Revolution, suffering was on a massive scale.

Both Winston Churchill and Adolf Hitler spoke of what had happened to the Armenian people and each drew important lessons from their tragic story.

For further study visit:
http://www.ppu.org.uk/genocide/

The victorious powers tried to absolve themselves of blame by pinning all the guilt on the vanquished. Germany and her allies were forced to sign various humiliating treaties and stripped of land, colonies and important assets such as coal. Little wonder then, that later on Hitler and the Nazis would often refer resentfully to the 'Diktat of Versailles'. Nations were exhausted and broken by war and as a consequence for a time, cut back on their military spending or looked for ways to save money. Airpower was considered as one value-for-money option, often less expensive than vast warships or housing, feeding and equipping soldiers. The British acquired Mesopotamia (modern day Iraq) from Ottoman Turkey and decided to use aircraft to subdue and control the country.

The harshness of treaties such as that of the Treaty of Versailles (1919) caused great resentment amongst the defeated people and sowed the seeds for future troubles and conflicts. Yet throughout the 1920s most nations were more concerned with economic woes.

Things to come

The 1930s saw a number of incidents that caused mounting concern around the war. After a few years of relative peace, the world seemed to be drifting towards war.

In 1933, the very year that Adolf Hitler and the Nazis came to power in Germany, the British writer, H.G.Wells (1866-1946) had published *The Shape of Things to Come.* This work of science fiction predicted future conflict and war, with cities being laid waste by aerial bombardment and vast numbers of civilian casualties and deaths.

Three years later a film version was made entitled *Things to Come* at a time when the power of aerial warfare was becoming more and more apparent. In 1935 the Italian Royal Air Force had strafed and bombed Abyssinia (Ethiopia) with poisoned gas as part of Fascist Italy's plans of conquest.

Nazi Germany's massive expansion of its airpower was to be put to the test when the *Luftwaffe* played a notorious role in the Spanish Civil War. Hitler supported Franco and the Nationalists in Spain's Civil War and sent out his Condor Legion to assist them by attacking Guernica. The raid was also an experiment and Guernica (a city in the Basque region of northern Spain) had been untouched by the Civil War up to April 1937.

The Condor Legion attacked in daylight and flew as low as 600 feet as it had no reason to fear any form of defence from the city. It was market day so the city centre was crowded. The first bombs fell on the city at 4.30pm when the main square in the city centre was hit. The first target of the bombers was a bridge that led into the city. The bombers that came in after the first wave, again targeted the city centre. By the time the raid was complete the centre of Guernica was in ruins and 1,654 people were killed and 889 wounded.

The Condor Legion returned in triumph.

From shockwaves to radio waves

The events in Spain and elsewhere and the evidence of Germany's growing military might was to prove a wake-up call for the British and other democracies.

The Guernica raid was to have enormous consequences. Both the Air Chief Marshal of the RAF (Sir Hugh Dowding) and the British Prime Minister, Neville Chamberlain, feared the possibility of a southern English city being similarly bombed.

This goes some way to explaining why Hitler was appeased in 1938, possibly to buy more time. It also encouraged Britain to modernise her outdated Royal Air Force and to expand her network of coastal defences.

As an island nation with the world's largest navy, Britain had long felt relatively secure. However, with the arrival of aviation and aerial warfare, fortress Britain seemed less secure.

During the First World War a series of air raids that began in 1915 (the first being at Great Yarmouth and King's Lynn) showed that the British Isles were no longer safe. The horrors of Guernica magnified the threat further and concentrated minds to meet the potential danger.

The 1930s were a troubled decade, the world was beset with economic problems and aggressor nations seemed intent on throwing their weight around. As well as the Spanish Civil War a wealth of other conflicts emerged:

- Imperial Japan invading China
- Fascist Italy invading Abyssinia (Ethiopia)
- Nazi Germany threatening her neighbours in Central Europe

The growing military muscle of Nazi Germany caused Britain particular anxiety and so it sought new ways to meet any threat. Whilst money was tight, government scientists (often known as 'boffins') worked to find a solution to the aerial danger. By the mid–1930s experiments were being conducted using radio waves and after a few false starts these looked promising.

Per ardua ad astra

What's in a motto?

From its earliest days even a Latin motto could not protect the RAF from those who saw an air force as of limited value.

No one can really understand the role of the Royal Air Force without knowing a little of how it was viewed and treated. In Britain, of three armed services the air force is the junior service and in its early days had a struggle to be taken seriously. Figures in the army and the navy felt that it had little relevance and some resented funds going to what was then the Royal Flying Corps (RFC). To begin with aviators were often seen as showmen, and so at the beginning of the First World War aircraft were mainly used for reconnaissance. Slowly as the aircraft became more reliable they were in a position to carry more armaments and so inflict more damage on the enemy, but even so, with the end of the First World War in 1918 many aircraft were scrapped and there was a real danger the air force would be disbanded altogether. So why did certain figures want to do away with the air force?

- The need to save money.
- Jealousy from the army and the navy.
- Some commanders believed that real military strength lay with the Army and Navy.
- A lack of understanding of the contribution aviation could play in the future.
- As an island nation it was felt that Britain's best defence was the navy.

The Royal Air Force (RAF) – the world's oldest independent air force was founded on 1st April 1918 by amalgamating the Royal Flying Corps and the Royal Naval Air Service.

Interestingly the motto chosen for the RAF was *Per ardua ad astra* which means 'Through Adversity (Struggles) to the stars'.

Defence on the cheap

Hard times for the RAF and fear of the threat from the air.

Luckily as the RAF was cheaper to run than either the army or navy it survived to play a role in controlling territories such as Mesopotamia (Iraq), although as the junior service it was often starved of investment. The 1920s saw cuts in military expenditure, which did not help the development of new technology.

Germany was forced to scrap its air force by the terms of the Treaty of Versailles (1919), but once Hitler and the Nazis came to power in 1933 a massive covert (secret) rebuilding programme was begun. A year earlier, back in Britain, the leader of the Conservative Party, Stanley Baldwin had delivered a key speech in the House of Commons (10/11/1932) when he expressed his opinion that in aerial warfare "the bomber will always get through".

This speech demonstrates just how fearful people were of the growing potential of aircraft. Some military figures felt it was better to spend resources on bombers rather than fighter aircraft, whilst other experts felt that air defence systems would largely be useless in the face of attack. Luckily there were others determined to use science to outwit potential enemy aircraft.

This General Election poster from 1935 demonstrates that people were becoming increasingly concerned about the danger of aerial attack.

The Boffins set to work

Slowly British military figures started to wake up to just how vulnerable the country was to attack. It was for the scientists to try and find solutions and create new ways of detecting enemy aircraft.

In the year 1934, a major air defence exercise was planned featuring a mock (pretend) attack on the country by aircraft. To the dismay of military officials over 50% of the bombers reached their targets without being challenged. This was even more alarming as those playing the defenders knew the intended routes in advance. It was clear to all that the military needed to address this weakness and quickly. The Army had for a while been experimenting with enormous concrete 'acoustic mirrors'. These strange devices located on an open windy stretch of coastline in Kent facing the English Channel were built of reinforced concrete and the aim was that they would act rather like sound locators, being large enough (in theory) to pick up the noise from an approaching aircraft.

Equipped with microphones they were designed to gather sound. The sound would then be focussed by means of a probe at the centre of the dish to a central listening position from which a bearing could be calculated. With data being collected from a number of these mechanisms it was believed that it would then be easier to calculate the direction the aircraft was travelling from.

The remains of sound mirrors, near Dungeness in Kent. A string of such ingenious devices were constructed along the south coast from Romney Marsh to Dungeness. Some were nearly 200 feet long.

A fatal flaw?

For all the science and ingenuity of the top secret devices Britain was working on, they were soon discovered to have weaknesses that caused alarm and some embarrassment. Yet all was not lost.

After some fine tuning the new devices were put to the test and sure enough they did pick up the sound of approaching aircraft. Sadly, that was not all; the huge sound mirrors happily gathered other sounds too, such as those of the local bird population, grazing sheep and even passing motor vehicles.

Dr H.E. Wimperis, the first Director of Scientific Research for the Air Ministry, and his assistant Mr A.P. Rowe decided to lay on a special demonstration for Air Marshal Dowding amongst others. When the day came there were red faces all round when the expensive equipment picked up the sound of a passing horse-drawn milk float!

The next idea was to try and develop some form of 'Death Ray'. Scientists were told to explore the possibility of using concentrated radio waves to melt aircraft metal or knock out or incapacitate the pilot. This idea was soon shown to be impossible by Robert Watson-Watt (Superintendent at the Radio Research Station, Slough), but he concluded that radio energy reflected off an aircraft could be detected.

Watson-Watt produced a significant document entitled *Detection and Location of Aircraft by Radio Methods* and believed that there were three areas worth exploring:

1. Reflected radio waves to detect aircraft
2. Radio – telephone communication between ground control and defending aircraft
3. Coded signal transmission between friendly aircraft

Such was the British Government's concern about the threat from air attack that a special committee was set up in 1934 under the chairmanship of Sir Henry Tizard – the Tizard Committee.

Left:
Sir Henry Tizard

Right:
Sir Robert Watson-Watt

Promising signs and the birth of Radar

Events in the Midlands were to give considerable encouragement and spur on further developments.

Air Marshal Sir Hugh Dowding had been following developments with interest. Dowding made it known that £10,000 would be made available if the system could be shown to have real potential. For the demonstration, it was decided to make use of transmissions from the powerful BBC short-wave station at Daventry and measure the power reflected from a Handley Page Heyford bomber (a bi-plane with a 75ft wingspan) flying up and down at various ranges. The Air Ministry officials sat in a specially adapted van where they watched as the signal indicated the aircraft (detection was achieved up to 8 miles). The experiment was a complete success and the money secured for more research. With the results having proved favourable further tests and refinements were needed to perfect the system so that it could differentiate between friendly and hostile aircraft – a considerable challenge.

> The new system was designated MOST SECRET and became known as Radio Detection Finding (RDF) and was treated as top secret. The term 'Radar' was not introduced until the Second World War.

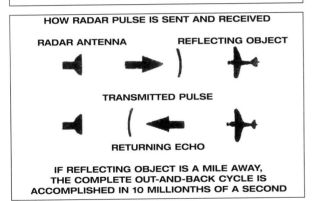

HOW RADAR PULSE IS SENT AND RECEIVED

RADAR ANTENNA   REFLECTING OBJECT

TRANSMITTED PULSE

RETURNING ECHO

IF REFLECTING OBJECT IS A MILE AWAY, THE COMPLETE OUT-AND-BACK CYCLE IS ACCOMPLISHED IN 10 MILLIONTHS OF A SECOND

The early success at Daventry now needed to be perfected and a chain of defences established. Who or what was the enemy that Britain was concerned about?

The Rise of the German menace

While Britain slowly explored new ideas, Nazi Germany was on a mission to become a major military power.

By the late 1920s Germany had an impressive civilian air service in the form of *Lufthansa*. *Lufthansa's* Chief Executive was a talented organiser called Erhard Milch. Under Milch's leadership Germany began developing new aircraft and once the Nazis came to power he soon became a key associate of his old friend Hermann Goering. When Adolf Hitler and the Nazis came to power in 1933, Hermann Goering was appointed Air Minister and a massive military expansion scheme was begun.

As a former pilot Goering naturally was keen to see the *Luftwaffe* play a major role in future conflicts and with this in mind convinced Hitler (if he needed any convincing) to massively increase expenditure on the research and development and production of aircraft. Initially because of restrictions placed on

Germany by the Treaty of Versailles, much of this was done in secret. The production numbers tell a remarkable story:

- 1932 – 36 planes
- 1933 – Hitler and Nazis come to power
- 1934 – 584 planes
- 1939 – 3,750 planes

By 1939 the Germans were capable of building 700 aircraft a month. Primarily they built large numbers of single or twin-engined bombers and dive bombers ... the reason for this was that they viewed the role of the *Luftwaffe* as aerial artillery, leading the attack and softening up the enemy ahead of the advancing forces of the *Wehrmacht* (German Army).

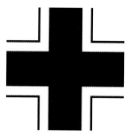

German inventiveness

With its strong tradition of inventiveness and appreciation of the value and potential of new technology, Germany soon developed some world beating aircraft.

Science and engineering has always been highly valued in Germany. Yet in the years immediately after Germany's defeat in 1918, resources were in short supply and the victorious powers controlled many of the country's resources, particularly connected with coal and steel. Strict controls were placed on what Germany could manufacture and so ingenuity was called for. One way of getting around certain restrictions was to focus on civilian aircraft and those deemed not to be for military use. A key figure in aircraft design in Germany was to be Wilhelm Emil Messerschmitt (1898-1978). Messerschmitt had been an air enthusiast from an early age and in the 1920s was to design a glider that set a world record.

He designed transport aircraft and with financial assistance from his wife bought the *Bayerische Flugzeugwerke* (Bavarian Aircraft Works) at Augsburg.

Fact - aircraft produced at Messerschmitt's factory carry the letters '*Bf*' e.g. The Messerschmitt *Bf* 109. Can you work out why?

Like all designers and engineers Messerschmitt was beset by setback and difficulties. Certainly, some of his new designs suffered technical difficulties and he had a difficult relationship with Erhard Milch which caused him problems. Although not particularly interested in politics he counted Rudolph Hess, the Deputy Leader of the Nazi Party as one of his friends. Of all the aircraft he was to design, his greatest was the Messerschmitt *Bf 109,* a potential world beater.

The Messerschmitt Bf 109 E – probably the Luftwaffe's most effective aircraft.

Germany rearms

With the coming of the Nazis it was clear that military spending was going to rise. New aircraft were to be a key element to this German expansion.

The first prototype Messerschmitt Bf 109 flew in 1935. This all-metal aircraft had a closed cockpit and a retractable under-carriage. Powered by a Rolls-Royce Kestrel V engine (later fitted with a Daimler Benz 601 engine), it had a maximum speed of 342 mph (550 km) and a range of 410 miles (660 km). It was 28ft 4in (8.65m) long with a wingspan of

32ft 4in (9.87m). The monoplane aircraft was armed with two machine-guns and two deadly 20mm cannons. It was clear that this was to be a highly effective weapon of war and would within a couple of years, be battle-tested during the Spanish Civil War. In 1939 it was the Bf 109 that enabled the *Luftwaffe* to push aside Polish air resistance to the German invasion. The following year it was the 109 that provided the air umbrella over the German's blitzkrieg advances. The Bf 109 was smaller than the British Spitfire and so more difficult to hit, plus it could fly at a slightly higher altitude which gave it the advantage of being able to attack from above.

Unbeknown to the British the Germans had also been experimenting with an early warning device and in some ways were ahead of what was going on in Britain. Ever since Hitler and the Nazis had come to power in 1933 there had been an enormous amount of money spent on the military and every aspect of research.

In a radio broadcast in 1936, *Reichsmarshall*

Hermann Goering, Commander-in-Chief of the *Luftwaffe,* made it quite clear what the regime's priorities were;

"Guns will make us powerful; butter will only make us fat."

Hermann Goering

Time for fine-tuning

As the Nazis prepared to flex their muscles, the leading democracies of Europe such as Britain began to wake up to the potential danger.

Following on from the success of the experiment at Daventry it was decided to carry out further top secret experiments at Orford

Ness in Suffolk on the east coast of England from May 1935. A series of aerials were erected on 75ft masts and initially detection could be made up to 17 miles, but with some fine tuning this was increased to 40 miles. Soon radar was being perfected to help calculate map positions and an aircraft's height. So important were these developments that Watson-Watt became convinced that a chain of radar stations needed to be constructed along the east coast (the most likely direction from which the 'enemy' would attack). These radar stations would work as follows:

- Give warning of imminent attack.
- Tell fighter aircraft where to engage the enemy.
- Give an indication of the number of enemy aircraft.
- Provide data that would help in plotting the intended target.
- Would enable defensive fighters to be 'scrambled' and be instructed where to engage the enemy.

Watson-Watt proposed that a full-scale station be built, followed by a cluster of stations to cover the Thames Estuary (to protect London) and others to protect the east and south coast of England. Permission was granted for five, with more to follow. All information collected was to be combined with other data gathered by the Observer Corps (later the Royal Observer Corps).

The move to Bawdsey Manor

On 16th September 1935 the Air Defence Committee of the Committee for Imperial Defence sanctioned its purchase as the centre for research work and also as the headquarters for the organisation of a chain of stations (some 10 miles down the coast from Orford Ness). All of this had happened within months and with a research headquarters having been established at Bawdsey Manor on the Suffolk Coast, it became clear that a potential threat was finally being taken very seriously.

Visit the following website to find out more about Bawdsey Manor and its role in the development of radar:
www.bawdseymanor.co.uk

www.suffolktouristguide.com/Bawdsey-Radar-Station.asp

Bawdsey soon became a hive of activity where scientists and military figures worked tirelessly to perfect their equipment and techniques. In order to gather further data on the effectiveness of the equipment, work began on plotting civil airliners flying into Croydon. During 1936 a trial was held where a KLM flight was selected and a perfect 'interception' was made. The RAF fighters involved continued on course to counter the impression that they had come out to meet it. The secrecy surrounding what was going on meant that it was essential to avoid suspicion and so no further interceptions of civil aircraft were made. Yet on the strength of the results being obtained Watson-Watt was able to convince the Government to set aside ten million pounds for a coastal chain of stations, an astronomical sum in those days.

Further experimentation was carried out to design a system for airborne use. A fairly crude device was fitted into an Anson aircraft and first tested during the summer of 1937 and in the autumn of that year managed to detect *HMS Courageous* and *HMS Rodney* at ranges in excess of 5 miles even in bad weather conditions.

Real potential

Defence Officials, military top brass and senior Civil Servants were beginning to realise the significance of Radio Detection Finding and further tests were soon authorised.

The work in Suffolk helped Henry Tizard to encourage the RAF based at Biggin Hill in Kent to investigate fighter control and interception techniques. Whilst the results concerning the possible interception of mass raids during daylight were encouraging there was increasing concern about the attacks that might take place at night using dispersed aircraft.

This problem was to be overcome by installing fairly basic equipment in fighter aircraft which after a few hiccups, proved capable of detecting aircraft and even naval vessels some miles off. To meet the potential challenge of low flying enemy aircraft, further solutions needed to be found.

The boffins set to work again to master another challenge and came up with the idea of an extensive network of radar standards.

These were to be a series of standard Chain Home radar stations (CH) and Chain Home Low radar stations (CHL), the CHL stations were set at a different frequency and so were better able to detect low flying aircraft. In some locations there was to be a combination of both types. Near the base of each of the radar towers was a hut where the operators monitored the signals.

A photograph taken in 1940 that shows Chain Home (CH) radar towers. The three towers on the left are the transmitters and those on the right are the receivers.

The Father of RADAR and the microwave oven

Robert Watson-Watt (1892-1973) was born in Scotland. He graduated with a Batchelor of Science degree. After university Watson-Watt worked with Professor William Peddie and as a result he developed a fascination with radio waves.

During the First World War he worked as a meteorologist at the Royal Aircraft Factory trying to use radio waves to locate the whereabouts of severe weather so that pilots could be forewarned.

After the war Watson-Watt moved to the Radio Research Station at Slough. In 1927, this organisation merged with the National Physics Laboratory (NPL) and Watson-Watt became a superintendent within this unit.

In February 1935, he produced a report entitled *The Detection and Location of Aircraft by Radio Methods*. This report impressed Sir Henry Tizard and his committee concerned with air defence. In February 1935, Watson-Watt took part in a successful trial in which short wave radio was used to detect a bomber.

Watson-Watt was put in charge of Bawdsey Manor, Suffolk. The work done by Watson-Watt and his team at Bawdsey led to the creation of a chain of radar stations along the east and south coast of England. This system,

known as Chain Home and Chain Home Low, was to play a vital part in the defence of Britain.

In 1940 knowledge was further enhanced at the University of Birmingham by the invention of the cavity magnetron.

This produced a compact source of short-wave radio waves and allowed Fighter Command to detect incoming enemy planes from a much greater distance. The magnetrons were also found to have another use - they could be used to heat up water.

Fact - Magnetrons are used as the source of heat in microwave ovens.

Robert Watson-Watt was awarded a knighthood in 1942.

Appeasement

As the storm clouds began to gather, Britain feared tackling the problem of Nazi and Fascist aggression.

By the mid-1930s it was clear that both Nazi Germany and Fascist Italy were on a path of military expansion and possible aggression. Having been so scarred by the horrors of the First World War, public opinion in Britain was largely supportive of a policy of appeasement.

So what exactly was appeasement?

Appeasement could be defined as:

"to *yield or concede to the belligerent demands (of a nation, group, person, etc.) in a conciliatory effort, sometimes at the expense of justice or other principles*"

This was a policy largely followed by the British Government moreso from 1937, especially with regards to Nazi Germany and Fascist Italy.

Neville Chamberlain became British Prime Minister on 28th May 1937 and he believed that by agreeing to some of the demands being made by Adolf Hitler (Germany) and Benito Mussolini (Italy), he could avoid a European war. At the time many people thought that Chamberlain was right and groups such as the Peace Pledge Union lobbied hard for war to be avoided. Chamberlain worked tirelessly to negotiate, almost certainly to buy more time, knowing full well that Britain was not anywhere near ready to defend herself against the growing might of Germany.

Neville Chamberlain

Adolf Hitler

Benito Mussolini

Shock waves and the RAF's response

Events in Spain were to demonstrate just how important defence was going to be. For Britain, radar was to be designed to work with fighter aircraft such as the Hurricane and Spitfire.

In April 1937 the *Luftwaffe* was to lay waste the Spanish town of Guernica. This horrifying example of the power of aerial bombardment acted as a wake-up call if one was needed. Britain responded by increasing aircraft manufacture. Many of the RAF's aircraft were hopelessly out of date, many being biplanes made from canvas and wood, hardly a match for the type of aircraft Messerschmitt was manufacturing in Germany.

Two British fighter planes that were to make their appearance during the Second World War were the Hurricane and the Spitfire.

- The Hawker Hurricane – designed by Sydney Camm (1893-1966). This was a single-seater monoplane powered by a Rolls Royce Merlin engine. The Hurricane could be refuelled and re-armed in half the time required for the Spitfire. Interestingly the fact that the early Hurricanes were fabric-covered meant that they were often more resistant to exploding cannon shells than the Spitfire.

- The Supermarine Spitfire – designed by Reginald J Mitchell (1895-1937). This was an all-metal single-seater fighter plane powered by a Rolls Royce Merlin engine. The Spitfire was particularly aerodynamic and was faster than the Hurricane. The Spitfire was a revolutionary aircraft; the ease of hand-ling made it very popular with pilots.

As Britain slowly prepared for the possibility of war it was fortunate to have Air Chief Marshal Sir Hugh Dowding overseeing a number of areas. Dowding recognised the importance of defensive measures and he was one of the first people to see and realise the potential of radar.

Farsighted individuals

Whilst Neville Chamberlain worked for peace, others knew that it was only a matter of time until war broke out.

Dowding in his role as Chief of Fighter Command ensured that radar was put to good use and that radar stations were placed in strategic locations, especially along the south and east coast of England. The fact that he believed in defence systems was important, especially as his vision and leadership helped prepare Britain for future attack. Increasingly fighter planes were also given priority, the number of fighter squadrons rose from thirteen (about 208) in 1936, to thirty-nine squadrons (about 624) by September 1939.

Since 1936 there had been four key command structures in the RAF:
Training, Bomber, Coastal and Fighter.

For some time the Conservative politician and writer Winston Churchill (1874-1965) had been warning of the dangers of Hitler's Germany.

Many people, even in his own political party ignored his dire warnings, but Churchill held true to his own beliefs. He was a staunch critic of appeasement and believed that it was essential that Britain rearm as quickly as possible. London as the world's largest city in 1939 was certain to be a target.

A quotation from Winston Churchill; "An appeaser is one who feeds a crocodile – hoping it will eat him last."

By 1938 the situation in Europe had deteriorated so much that the British Government was so concerned about possible air-raids that it had thousands of cardboard coffins made and believed it would require over two and half thousand extra hospital beds for the casualties. Air Raid Precaution (ARP) committees were established and thousands of gas masks issued. War looked increasingly likely and so Chamberlain made a number of last ditch efforts to negotiate with Hitler.

The Second World War begins

September 1939 was to finally see the policy of appeasement in tatters. War was to be declared and the moment had arrived when Britain's defences were to be put to the ultimate test.

Britain had already offered to protect Poland if it was attacked.

Things looked even more gloomy, when in August 1939 Germany signed a treaty with Communist Russia (The Nazi-Soviet Pact) - this now meant that Germany would be in a better position to attack Poland. Hitler, confident that neither Britain nor France would challenge him, decided to order the invasion of Poland ... yet to his surprise Britain and France gave him an ultimatum – if Germany did not withdraw from Poland by 3rd September Britain and France would declare war.

The Germans did not withdraw – the Second World War had begun.

How most Britons heard the news: "My long struggle to win peace has failed. I have to tell you now ... this country is at war with Germany."

Prime Minister Neville Chamberlain's radio broadcast to the nation, 11.15 am, 3rd September 1939.

"The war can end only with Hitler's elimination or the defeat of Britain." - Diary entry for 3rd September 1939. Count Ciano, Italian Minister of Foreign Affairs.

4th September 1939, London - King George VI addresses the British people over the wireless (radio) on September 4, 1939, one day after Britain declared war on Nazi Germany. He asked them to "stand calm, firm, and united" against what was to come. (Image by © Hulton-Deutsch Collection/CORBIS).

Preparing for the worst

Initial fear was replaced by a lull in activities when the 'Phoney War' took place. At least the lull gave additional time to prepare for a possible German onslaught.

As part of Britain's preparation for a possible war some 38 million gas masks were issued and plans were drawn up to evacuate children from London. Poland was soon crushed and there was little that Britain or France could do.

Many Britons believed that the dangers of war and especially aerial bombardment had been exaggerated and they began to resent having to carry gas masks and blackout their homes at night. Soon people starting calling it 'the Phoney War' and became almost casual about things.

By now Winston Churchill (a critic of the policy of appeasement) had joined the Government, but he was not happy about how the Chamberlain Government was running things.

When the Germans attacked Denmark and Norway, British and some French troops were landed in Norway, but failed to halt the German advance.

Conservative MPs started to criticise their own leader and finally on 10th May 1940 Neville Chamberlain resigned and King George VI invited Winston Churchill to form a new government. He immediately set about preparing for the ultimate challenge, not only in planning the defence of Britain, but maintaining the country's morale.

On the very day that he became Prime Minister the Germans launched their *blitzkrieg* (lightning war), invading Holland, Belgium and Luxembourg and sweeping in to France.

It was clear to all that this was no 'Phoney War' ... Britain would have to fight for its very survival.

1940 – the fateful year

Events on the Continent of Europe now meant that Britain seemed doomed. German military might seemed unstoppable and even some of Britain's friends believed the Germans would win.

With the invasion of France the *Luftwaffe* soon destroyed the bulk of France's airforce. The RAF sent backup in the shape of some 400 bombers and fighters, yet by mid-May the RAF had lost 205 aircraft and the French Government were asking for more help, something Dowding wanted to resist for fear of weakening the defence of Britain. Dowding was over-ruled and an additional ten squadrons were sent to France.

With further German advances British, French and Belgian forces were soon isolated at Dunkirk, the RAF did what it could to help and actually shot down 240 enemy planes for the loss of 170. That said, troops on the ground complained that more should have been done by the 'Brylcreem Boys' (a nickname for men in the RAF). With the evacuation of Dunkirk, and the Fall of France, Britain stood alone.

It was clear that it was only a matter of time before a vicious onslaught was unleashed on Britain and it was going to be a matter of life and death.

The RAF was to play a vital role in protecting the nation, the question was could it withstand the power of the *Luftwaffe?*

> *"In some almost supernatural way the Prime Minister had felt the pulse of the country and heard its heartbeat."*
>
> *Oliver Lyttelton, Viscount Chandos describing Churchill following Dunkirk in 'The Memoirs of Lord Chandos', published in 1962.*

Britain at the ready?

The RAF and RADAR now had to be ready for their greatest test. Preparation and planning were crucial.

Fighter Command was to be at the forefront of operations and it was organised into a series of groups, each of which was responsible for an area of Britain. These groups were then subdivided into sectors and each sector had a main fighter base with other satellite fighter bases. The main fighter base for each sector had an operations room with maintenance and repair facilities for the aircraft.

Dowding had wisely used his position to ensure that many grass runways were replaced with concrete. He had also organised Britain's aerial defences into four groups:

- The Fighter Command groups were to be as follows:

10 Group covered Wales and the south-west of England. It was commanded by Air Vice-Marshal Sir Quintin Brand.

11 Group covered London and the south-east and did a great deal of the fighting in the famous battle. 11 Group was commanded by Air Vice-Marshal Keith Park.

12 Group, commanded by Air Vice-Marshal Trafford Leigh-Mallory, controlled the industrial Midlands, East Anglia and northern England up to Yorkshire and Lancashire.

13 Group covered parts of northern England not covered by 12 Group and southern Scotland and Northern Ireland. It was commanded by Air Vice-Marshal Richard Saul.

Central to each sector and group was Bentley Priory in Stanmore, Middlesex (the Headquarters of Fighter Command). All data on attacks from enemy planes was to be gathered by the radar stations and the Royal Observer Corps and then it was decided how to react.

Softening up

August 1940 was to see the beginning of events which were to become known as the Battle of Britain. This was meant to be the prelude to full scale invasion.

The German army had proved its valour, now the *Luftwaffe* was to have its day. Reich Marshal Hermann Goering had often boasted of the superiority of German airpower and was keen to put it to the test. In July 1940 German bombers began to attack British ports and various skirmishes took place over the skies of southern England. The RAF knew that they were now the guardians of England and it was up to them to give the Third Reich a bloody nose. The aerial attacks were all meant to help prepare things for Operation Sea Lion (*Unternehmen Seelöwe*) – an invasion of Britain by sea. Hitler had never been particularly keen on the idea of invading Britain, but had been convinced that Britain's defiance would thwart his other plans (he was far more interested in the forthcoming attack on Russia).

Operation Sea Lion was essentially as follows:

- Gain air superiority by knocking out radar stations and the bulk of the RAF.
- Then an amphibious three pronged invasion comprising:
  a) Army Group A (some 6 divisions) invading Kent
  b) Army Group A (some 4 divisions) invading Sussex and Hampshire
  c) Army Group B (some 3 divisions) invading Dorset

The success of this plan relied on Germany having control of the English Channel. The *Luftwaffe* needed to be able to neutralise the RAF so that German troop ships could cross the Channel safely. German tacticians believed the RAF to be weak and the British position to be largely hopeless. Britain had lost a large amount of military hardware on the beaches of Dunkirk and so looked supremely vulnerable.

The moment of truth

With invasion imminent it was clear that radar would be put to its ultimate test. The battle for Britain's very survival was about to begin.

If the Germans were going to be completely successful they would need:- control of the English Channel, control of the skies and good weather.

Fact - Never underestimate the role that weather has played in military history – it can often be a decisive factor – both Napoleon and Hitler's plans for invading Russia were to come unstuck because of the weather.

In 1939 Nazi Germany had approximately 4,000 aircraft compared to Britain's 1,660 aircraft. It has been calculated that at the start of the Battle of Britain the *Luftwaffe* had over 2,500 serviceable aircraft on any normal day. The RAF in comparison had 1,200 aircraft, but only approximately 660 were serviceable. The RAF was also hampered by the fact that it had a shortage of trained and experienced pilots (a number had been killed during the Evacuation at Dunkirk).

Britain had a number of advantages over the *Luftwaffe*. Radar allowed Britain to track incoming enemy aircraft and so gave Fighter Command sufficient time to get its aircraft airborne. Radar also ensured that the Germans lost the element of surprise.

Fact - By early 1940, 51 radar bases had been constructed around the coast of south and eastern Britain. There were also over 1,000 Royal Observer Corps (ROC) posts manned and trained to spot German aircraft. www.therocmuseum.org.uk

---

Although the *Luftwaffe* had numerical supremacy it is important to note that British fighter planes could spend more time in the air over southern and eastern England as they could easily land for fuel, whereas the German fighters could not.

The German fighters were also limited in that they could not reload their guns if they ran out of ammunition while over England. Whilst the German bombers could fly long distances, their fighter aircraft could not fly as far and so this meant that German bombers were open to attack from the RAF's fighter aircraft.

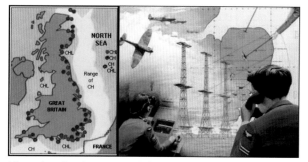
Map showing locatons of CH and CHL Radar Stations and the area covered. Courtesy of the National Archives

The Battle for Britain

Radar and the RAF were to be put to the severest test throughout the summer of 1940. If either failed, Britain would have fallen to Nazi Germany.

There was no definite date for the start of what became known as the **Battle of Britain**. There were few raids in early June 1940 and then on 10th July 1940, the *Luftwaffe* attacked shipping convoys in the Channel Ports. They also attacked a series of radar masts along the south coast.

The *Luftwaffe* used Junkers Ju 87 – the notorious Stuka dive-bombers ... whilst these were highly accurate they were vulnerable to attack from the more manoeuvrable Hurricanes and Spitfires. The Germans were testing for weak points, which they hoped to exploit later.

Day after day RAF pilots flew countless sorties and dog-fights over southern England and the Channel coast. This first phase of the battle lasted until about 11th August (see "The attempt to 'silence' radar"). The RAF appeared heavily outnumbered and this convinced Hermann Goering that Britain's defeat was imminent (wisely Dowding was keeping a number of aircraft in reserve).

By the end of July, the RAF had lost a total of 150 aircraft while the *Luftwaffe* had lost 268. In August, the *Luftwaffe* started to attack Fighter Command's airfields, radar stations and operation rooms. This tactic was aimed at destroying the RAF on the ground so that the *Luftwaffe* did not need to fight them in the air. Without radar the RAF would be seriously hampered in terms of early warning and the destruction of operation rooms would cut off communications between fighter bases and those at the heart of the battle controlling the movement of fighter planes. Destroyed runways would hamper the chances of a fighter plane taking off.

Bad weather stopped the *Luftwaffe* from daily raids in August, but August 15th is seen as a key date as nearly all the Stuka dive-bombers were destroyed by this date as they fell easy prey to the British fighter planes. Therefore, pin-point bombing of radar stations was all but impossible.

Junkers 88 bomber, the Scourge of Guernica

From August 23rd to September 6th, the *Luftwaffe* started night time bombing raids on cities. The RAF was also badly hit with 6 out of 7 main fighter bases in south-eastern England being put out of action.

Biggin Hill was wrecked. However, for all this apparent success, the *Luftwaffe* was losing more planes than the RAF - 1,000 German losses to 550 British.

Radar on active service

The Battle of Britain saw Radar come into its own. The edge it gave, along with a change of German tactics, undoubtedly helped save the day.

The essential data collected by the radar network along with the information supplied by the Royal Observer Corps was vital. The wealth of material was fed through to Bentley Priory where it was sifted and transferred onto a large map in the form of red counters (enemy aircraft) and black counters (friendly aircraft). The time bought by radar was crucial and allowed a raft of calculations to be made and precious resources deployed as effectively as possible.

Make no mistake the RAF was being hideously punished and losing dozens of young pilots. Yet just as numbers were falling dangerously low, Goering made a fundamental error, when he ordered a change of tactics.

Instead of continuing to pound RAF bases and radar stations the *Luftwaffe* started bombing British cities. In doing so the Germans gave Fighter Command time to recover from its losses and for pilots to recover from the many hours a day they operated, which took many to the brink of exhaustion.

Hitler's Deputy, Goering had always boasted that Berlin would never be bombed, so when RAF planes retaliated for the bombing of London, the German people were deeply shocked. Hitler was furious and believing that the RAF was effectively finished, ordered the *Luftwaffe* to begin bombing Britain's key cities.

With London very much in the firing line the RAF and the people of Britain were fortunate to have Air Vice-Marshal Sir Keith Park as the commander of 11 Group. This New Zealander was a calm man, who used his forces with great care. The Germans mistakenly thought the RAF had few reserves and yet Park used resources effectively, punishing the German aircraft seeking to punish London.

Fact - Air Vice-Marshal Sir Keith Park played a pivotal role in the defence of London. www.sirkeithpark.com

The attempt to 'silence' radar

The Germans were aware of radar, in point of fact some of the earliest experiments with the use of radio waves had taken place in Germany.

> **Fact -** In 1888 the German, Heinrich Hertz had discovered that radio waves could be bounced off objects.

German Intelligence was aware that the British had developed some form of radar system, although they were not fully aware that there was a nationwide system (the Chain Home network had been completed in the spring of 1939 and began a 24 hour 'watch' for enemy aircraft).

During the early stages of the Battle of Britain the *Luftwaffe* launched some devastating raids on radar stations. On 11th August 1940 one particular raid included 100 Junkers Ju88s, 120 Messerschmitt BF110s and 25 Messerschmitt BF109s. 20 Junkers Ju88s broke off to attack Chain Home radar at Ventnor, the Isle of Wight. Although the German aircraft were intercepted by Spitfires from 152 Squadron, some 15 managed to get through and strafed and bombed the radar station, temporarily putting it out of action. A further raid took place 5 days later.

Interestingly, although the raid had been effective, German Intelligence assumed that there was no serious damage as the station still seemed to be emitting a signal – this caused the Germans to direct their attacks elsewhere – a costly blunder.

The radar station at Ventnor later provided vital training for a planned British raid on a German radar installation at Bruneval, France.

> The inscription on plaque marking the site of RAF Ventnor on the Isle of Wight, a World War II radar station, part of the Chain Home network ...
>
> VENTNOR AND DISTRICT
> LOCAL HISTORY SOCIETY
> SITE OF
> VENTNOR RADAR STATION
> (formerly RAF Ventnor)
>
> Built 1938, and repeatedly bombed from 1940, but functioned until the early 1960's

A Battle Won

The Blitz continued and yet it was clear the Luftwaffe's spirit had been broken and Britain had survived to fight another day.

For ordinary people the sight and sounds of Hurricanes and Spitfires taking on the enemy cheered them greatly and helped them to cope with the difficulties of daily life and night time raids.

Many military historians believe that by changing their tactics the Germans made a serious error, but at the time it was hard to appreciate that, especially when the sky was black with aircraft making for London. As the largest city in the world, with the busiest port, London was a prime target and soon the warehouses around the docks in the East End were ablaze, a beacon to attract further bombers with their deadly loads.

15th September 1940 saw the climax of the Battle of Britain, that day alone the *Luftwaffe* lost 79 aircraft and the RAF 36. It was clear, even to the ever boastful Goering, that the RAF had not been destroyed.

On September 17th, Hitler postponed indefinitely the invasion of Britain through the night time raids – the Blitz continued with London, Plymouth and Coventry suffering horrific raids.

In a continuation of the propaganda war, the British Government claimed that the RAF had shot down 2,698 German planes. The actual figure was 1,100. Both sides exaggerated the number of aircraft shot down. The RAF certainly lost 650 planes, not the 3,058 aircraft that the *Luftwaffe* claimed to have shot down - more than the entire RAF. Britain's victory proved that the German military machine was not invincible.

Fact - Approximately 80% of the German aircraft were shot down by Hurricanes.

So much owed

Heroism and suffering. Courage and sacrifice. Debt and Gratitude. The event we know of as 'the Battle of Britain' was to have far reaching consequences.

As the Germans turned away intent on attacking Russia, they had allowed Britain to fight on, to be a base from which the Allies a few years later could operate attacks on Nazi-occupied Europe and eventually defeat Hitler and his murderous regime.

Why was the *Luftwaffe* defeated?

- Radar played a key role and enabled the British to have advanced warning and react accordingly.
- British fighters could land, be refuelled and rearmed and back in the air quickly.
- The *Luftwaffe's* fighters could only spend a limited time over England before their fuel ran dangerously low.
- The British had some exceptional aircraft in the form of the Hurricane and Spitfire.
- By changing tactics the *Luftwaffe* gave Fighter Command vital breathing space.

> **Fact -** The Battle of Britain signalled a significant shift in US opinion of Britain's ability to survive.

Many young lives on both sides were lost. Some damaged forever with horrific physical and emotional scars. For many the late summer and autumn of 1940 was a turning point, one which lead Winston Churchill to deliver one of his most memorable speeches in tribute to the RAF:-

"The gratitude of every home in our Island, in our Empire, and indeed throughout the world, except in the abodes of the guilty, goes out to the British airmen who, undaunted by odds, unwearied in their constant challenge and mortal danger, are turning the tide of the World War by their prowess and by their devotion. Never in the field of human conflict was so much owed by so many to so few."

Radar research on the move

It is important to remember that the Germans were aware that the British were working on some form of radar. In the months just prior to war they had even sent an airship to spy on what was going on along the east coast of England. Once war had begun it was thought wise to relocate this highly sensitive work to Worth Matravers (4 miles west of Swanage) on the Isle of Purbeck, Dorset in southern England. This part of Dorset was chosen because it had a flat cliff top location and was ideal for testing radar. There were essentially two types of radar:-

1. Ground radar, which had a lower frequency. This was the responsibility of the Ministry of Supply.

2. Airborne radar, which had a higher frequency. This was the responsibility of the Ministry of Aircraft Production.

During the two years that the scientists and engineers were stationed in Dorset (May 1940 - May 1942) a number of improvements were made to radar.

> **Fact -** Radar at this time was still known as Radio Direction Finding, the word 'radar' did not come about until the Americans entered the war.

Stanley Abercrombie recalls his time as a Senior Scientific Officer working on Responder Beacons at Worth Matravers;

"We really felt we were at the forefront of things. Our work was certainly exciting. I even had the opportunity to go up in Stirling and Wellington bombers. Much of my time was spent on developing airborne radar that could 'interrogate' ground beacons used by resistance fighters in occupied France and Belgium. These were especially important when the RAF was trying to drop supplies and even SOE (Special Operation Executive) agents to the right place in Occupied Europe."

The Bruneval Raid and Pickford Removal lorries

With Radar proving so valuable it was essential to see how well advanced the German systems had become.

With the likes of Stanley Abercrombie and colleagues working on a transponding radar so that aircraft could 'interrogate' and even 'communicate' with the ground or potentially other aircraft, it was imperative to gain a greater understanding of what the Germans had developed. So in February 1942 British paratroopers of the 1st Airborne Division supported by the Royal Navy, launched a daring and wholly successful raid on German radar defences in northern France. They managed to capture some key pieces of equipment which demonstrated that German technology lagged somewhat behind that of the British.

After this raid had taken place Winston Churchill was fearful that the Germans might carry out a revenge attack and after a bombing raid took place on the Dorset coastal town of Swanage in May 1942 it was decided to move operations from Worth Matravers to Malvern in rural Worcestershire.

"The whole move was carried out in a day. I remember a fleet of Pickford Removal lorries arriving and transporting us to Worcestershire. The people in Malvern had no idea of what we were up to. I don't think the locals really approved, they must have wondered why we young men had not joined up." – remembers Stanley Abercrombie.

> **Fact -** the code name for the Bruneval Raid was 'Operation Biting'.

For the remainder of the war the Telecommunications Research Establishment (TRE) as it was called, was to remain billeted at Malvern College. Those scientists and engineers working at Malvern were very much on the frontline of developments in radar defence. The role they played in the Second World War cannot be overstated ... without their work its outcome might well have been very different.

Smoke and mirrors

The Second World War was to see mankind's ingenuity put to work not only to develop new devices, but also to outwit and deceive the enemy as never before.

Military history is rich with tales of secrets and deception. In classical times, the Greeks and Romans were past masters at using trickery and bluff. In India the famed King Chandragupta of the Mauryan dynasty donned a disguise to enter the camp of his enemies and in Shakespeare's play *Henry V*, the English monarch pretends to be a humble soldier to gather intelligence of the mood of his own men on the eve of the Battle of Agincourt. *The Art of War* by Sun Tzu, was written in China in the 6th century BC and is still one of the most famous books about military tactics.

Espionage, surveillance, bluff and counter bluff are very much the meat and drink of warfare. The Twentieth Century was to see the trickery, and the smoke and mirrors become ever complex and sophisticated. The need to outmanoeuver the enemy would demand ideas sometimes of cunning simplicity and at other times ideas that were intricate and taxing. Psychology was to be employed, as well as the very latest gadgetry.

> *"All warfare is based on deception. Hence when able to attack, we must seem unable; when using our forces, we must seem inactive; when we are near we must make the enemy believe we are far away; when we are far away, we must make him believe that we are near. Hold out baits to entice the enemy. Feign disorder, and crush him."*
>
> from *The Art of War* by Sun Tzu

Winston Churchill talked of the race for electronic superiority as 'the Wizard War'. War demanded strategy, guile and plenty of lateral thinking.

Forewarned is Forearmed

The need to keep things hidden was paramount. In an age of total war secrets were to be a necessity, one akin to survival.

The development of Radar had already demonstrated how important innovation could be. Interestingly the Germans did have an idea of what the British were up to and were formulating similar ideas of their own.

The cloak of secrecy helps hide what you know, as well as what you do not know. All of the warring powers were eager to keep things secret to gain advantage and ultimately to secure victory. The truth itself could prove fatal by undermining morale or allowing the enemy psychological advantage.

This need for secrecy along with constant propaganda was a common feature of the Second World War not just in dictatorships such as Germany, Italy, Japan and Russia, but also in democracies such as Britain and America.

Britain's wartime Prime Minister was candid about the need to deceive;

"In wartime, truth is so precious that she should always be attended by a bodyguard of lies." Comments made to Joseph Stalin, the Dictator of Soviet Russia at the Tehran Conference in 1943.

The motto of the Royal Observer Corps, who played such an important part in the Battle of Britain is *Forewarned is Forearmed* and this in many ways could be the motto of all those seeking to gain advantage in wartime. That said, it is important to remember that secrecy continues in peacetime; vigilance is an ongoing process.

"Qui desiderat pacem, praeparet bellum." – Let him who wants peace, prepare for war. The words of the Vegetius, a Roman writing in the 4th Century AD.

The side with the element of surprise on its side could gain an advantage, one which might well result in them 'winning' the war.

The need for secrecy

In an age of ready access to wireless technology there was not only a wealth of opportunities to listen in to others, but also to be listened in to.

With the coming of the wireless (radio) came a host of amateur wireless enthusiasts who even with a relatively simple short wave radio set, were in a position to listen in to others. This meant that there was a desperate need for intelligence and military communication to be encrypted.

As with all highly sensitive information there were those who would go to extreme lengths to get access to it. During any conflict each side needed to be sent and receive messages containing information about troop movements and future attacks. It was essential that the messages were put into code so that if they were intercepted by the enemy their meaning could not be understood. If codes could be broken it would be possible to discover the enemy's plans.

There was also an added possibility that if a code could be cracked without the enemy's knowledge then it might be possible to feed false information to enemy forces using their own code.

One thing was for certain, any such operations would be hush hush. Lives, even the fate of entire nations depended on the covert work being done – the stakes were indeed extraordinarily high and even now we do not necessarily know the full story, and probably never will.

For all the wealth of articles, books and films about the Second World War this secret aspect remains largely unexplored and only in recent years have historians begun to appreciate just how vital a role it played.

The need for secrecy has ensured that some of the stories have literally been taken to the grave. Secrets have remained exactly that.

Wireless war in its infancy

Whilst wireless communication was relatively new it was soon to prove its worth.

In the latter years of the Nineteenth Century the Italian inventor Guglielmo Marconi (1874-1937) had invented a new means of communication, that of wireless telegraphy, and this evolved into the radio. Military leaders soon recognized the value of this technology.

In the years just prior to the First World War, the military began to use wireless communication to crack coded messages sent by foreign governments.

The War Office in London (now called the Ministry of Defence) established its own code-breaking unit – MI1b, often choosing to employ academics who relished the challenge of deciphering a coded message.

Once the First World War had started the Royal Navy established its own code-breaking section in Room 40 of the Admiralty Old Buildings, Whitehall, London. Room 40 had one of its greatest successes when it managed to decipher the so-called Zimmermann Telegram.

> "Written by the German foreign minister Arthur Zimmermann, the telegram suggested that Mexico should join the war on Germany's side in return for 'generous financial support and an undertaking on our part that Mexico is to re-conquer the lost territory in Texas, New Mexico and Arizona'. Its publication in US newspapers finally persuaded America to end its isolation and join the war, thereby ensuring the defeat of Germany." – From *Station X* by Michael Smith, Channel 4 Books, 1998.

Code-breaking had not only proved its military value, it had also shown that it had political worth as well and ensured that funding would be made available for its work.

In 1919 the British Government decided to amalgamate MI1b and Room 40 into the Government Code and Cipher School (GC&CS) and from 1926 GC&CS shared the same building as the Secret Intelligence Service (SIS).

Radio Monitoring

The potential for radio monitoring had been recognized by all the major powers, each designing systems to seek to outwit others.

Germany with its particular appreciation and expertise in the area of electronics, soon capitalised on developments in the field of wireless communication. The German Naval Monitoring Service (*Funkbeobachtungsdienst*) better known as *B-Dienst* had proved highly effective. After 1919 Germany was forced to drastically reduce its military activities and further economic woes ensured that what work was being done, was small scale. Then after the Nazis came to power in 1933 spending on defence was massively increased and that included surveillance not only of foreign powers, but also of the civilian population. Radio Monitoring enabled Germany to gain an understanding of British convoy tactics at sea and its preparations to deal with the potential submarine threat and all of this was before the outbreak of the Second World War.

It is important to realise that all the world powers were engaged in some form of radio monitoring, invariably with mixed results. European powers such as Britain and France with vast empires required a network of listening posts to endeavour to protect colonies and trading routes. The USA as an emerging power, was increasingly interested in what was happening in the Pacific and Far East where Japan appeared to be undergoing a massive military expansion. It was not just about monitoring potential enemies, but also about gaining an insight into the mindsets and policies of neutral states and even allies. With a wealth of top secret data being transmitted, countries and their armed forces often resorted to developing a range of coding systems depending on how important the information was. The keys to less complex coding systems were often cracked with relative ease.

Question: Why might countries monitor their own allies?

The Birth of Enigma

Often a welter of seemingly mundane information had to be deciphered and this had to be waded through and sifted to discover what had real significance. To encrypt in the first place could be an arduous process and so governments were anxious to find devices capable of improving the efficiency and effectiveness of the coding process. In the very year of Germany's humiliation at Versailles a Dutchman, Hugo Koch, patented a new cipher machine. The patent for this machine was bought by a German engineer Dr Arthur Scherbius, who made a number of improvements and within a couple of years his machine called *Enigma* was being marketed as a business tool designed to keep commercial messages.

Enigma was an intriguing mechanism, it looked like a cross between a cash register

Fact - to this very day companies around the world fear competitors gaining access to commercial sensitive material.

and a portable typewriter. It was powered by batteries and featured a series of rotors that were adjustable, these enciphered the letters typed in by the operator. To add to its complexity it was essential that both the sender's and the receiver's machines had to be set in the same way – quite some feat as there were so many variables.

"There were sixty possible orders in which the wheels could be placed in the machine, with a total of 17,576 different position settings for each wheel. The plugboard allowed 150 million million changes of circuit. The total number of possible settings for a basic German Enigma cipher machine was, therefore, 159 million million million." – From *Station X* by Michael Smith, Channel 4 Books, 1998.

Fact - *Enigma* had the added advantage that could avoid showing the use of 'favourite' letters. In English for instance 'E' appears most often.

What makes an ideal code breaker?

As encrypting machines became ever more complex it was essential to employ the finest minds to find the key to such encrypting.

Just as there were countless variables when it came to codes and code systems, it is equally true that code breakers were not of a standard type. Naturally, it was essential that they were intelligent people, the sort of people who could think laterally and were not daunted by the prospect of the challenge that faced them. In Britain the security services looked to the elite universities such as Oxford and Cambridge for many of the finest brains. At interviews possible candidates were asked about their hobbies and interests, as well as their proficiency at languages and mathematics. Those who could read music, play chess and enjoyed crossword puzzles were at a distinct advantage.

Think for a moment about the ability to comprehend and understand complex ideas, to solve puzzles and to anticipate and predict what someone else might do next. A modern code breaker could just as easily play *Scrabble*, enjoy *Sudoku*, design computer programmes and find *Countdown* conundrums a doddle.

The sort of person who was good at anagrams, assimilated facts with ease, or was a prodigious reader might be the ideal candidate. Alan Stripp in his book entitled *Code Breaker in the Far East* (Oxford University Press 1995) recalls the following;

Challenge: See how many words you can make out of the letters featured in the word *intelligence* in 60 seconds.

"The interview was friendly but searching. There was none of the expected emphasis on proficiency at sport, or on grit, gristle and leadership. What had I done at school? What languages had I studied? Latin, Greek, French, a little German. With what result? What were my motives?"

Bletchley Park

With war looming Britain's cryptanalysts moved out of London to a new home that soon became a hive of activity.

In 1938 Bletchley Park, a rambling Victorian country house in Buckinghamshire, some 50 miles north-west of London was chosen to be the home of the secret Government Code and Cipher School (GC&CS). Bletchley was to be the centre of British code-breaking during the war. The code-breakers that were based there were specially chosen from the cleverest people in the land – many from Oxford and Cambridge universities (interestingly Cambridge graduates far outnumbered those from Oxford). Many were brilliant linguists or mathematicians, some were somewhat eccentric, yet all were dedicated to their task.

The house was soon packed with offices, the main body of GC&CS (including its Army, Navy and Air Sections) was on the house's ground floor complete with a telephone exchange, a teleprinter room, kitchen and dining room. A wireless room was set up in the water tower and this was given the code name *Station X*. Soon Bletchley became crammed and a series of wooden huts were erected in the grounds to provide additional basic offices for all the staff who were to play their part in the wireless war.

> **Fact -** Admiral Sir Hugh Sinclair (Director of Naval Intelligence, Head of MI6, and the founder of the Government Code and Cipher School) had bought the mansion with his own money for £7,500.

Life at Bletchley Park

Once the Second World War began, Bletchley Park (BP) was to be a nerve centre of operations. BP became a place where men and women worked in shifts, seemingly day and night endeavouring to solve the keys to codes being used by the enemy. Soon hundreds, then thousands of individuals toiled in small wooden and concrete huts often oblivious to the activities going on in the room or hut next door. Secrecy was paramount and incredibly the Germans and the other Axis powers (such as Italy and later Japan) were ignorant of what was going on. Those who worked there were utterly dedicated to their work. Some of the work was undoubtedly repetitive and rather tedious, but nevertheless important – some staff worked on filing away a wealth of data whilst others were operating code-breaking machines.

Data was being fed into Bletchley from a whole variety of sources.

Left: General Heinz Guderian in his armoured personnel carrier operating an early enigma machine in France, May 1940.

"I was a Voluntary Interceptor with the Radio Security Service. During the daytime I worked at Marconi's Wireless Telegraph Co., at Hackbridge near Mitcham in Surrey on radio receivers for the RAF's bombers, but from 8.00 to 10.00pm Monday to Friday, I listened on my radio receiver for Morse code signals and copied the encoded messages down on special log sheets and message forms. All this information I sent to "PO Box 25, Barnet, Herts" by post and did not know until 1980 that the messages I had copied were sent from Barnet by dispatch rider to Bletchley Park were they decoded.

I learnt, after 1980, that some of the messages that I had intercepted were from a network used by the German Secret Service and the Gestapo to contact the German embassies around the world." - Raymond Fautley, C.Eng., MIET.

Bletchley Park in 1926

Purposeful, but not glamorous

All too often the work of those seeking to intercept codes, or break their keys was monotonous.

As the World War became ever more global it was essential that the traffic of secret messages and information was decoded, interpreted and monitored. For an island nation such as Britain it was vital to track the activities of the German navy, especially its deadly fleet of U-boats (submarines). Such work was especially important during the Battle of the Atlantic which lasted the whole length of the war (1939 - 1945). The messages transmitted to and from U-boats were intercepted by Royal Air Force 'listening stations', these were known as 'Y' Stations. Equipped with tall aerials they could pick up radio signals being transmitted as far away as eastern Russia and the Pacific. In each 'Y' Station there was a team of Morse code operators whose job it was to listen in to coded messages and record these. In cramped conditions the code operator would translate the Morse signals into letters and record these as quickly as possible (some of the best operators could record 90 letters a minute). Accuracy was paramount, as even the slightest error would ensure that the code breakers could not really do their work.

Those who had to break codes or messages were often helped by the fact that certain phrases were often used time and time again. Here are some examples:

- *Keinebesondere Ereignisse* (nothing to report)

- *Heil Hitler!*

Those recording messages rarely had any idea of exactly how the information was going to be used. All they knew was that they were playing their part in the war effort. Many amateur radio enthusiasts (known as 'Radio Hams') helped the work of 'Y' Stations by being enrolled as Voluntary Interceptors. The very best direction finding (d/f) operators were able to locate the origin of signals in under 10 seconds!

The Polish Contribution

Poland had good reason to want to monitor the activities of its neighbours not least because over the centuries it had suffered countless invasions and occupations.

During the 1920s and 30s the Poles had established the highly effective *Biuro Szyfrów* (Polish for 'Cipher Bureau'). The Poles used a number of French contacts in Berlin to acquire sensitive information that enabled them to construct a copy of the German Enigma machine.

As early as 1933 they had begun to crack German Army signals. France also had reason to fear her German neighbour and so was happy to work closely with Poland and with Britain and as the storm clouds of war gathered British, French and Polish cryptanalysts met in Paris in early 1939 and in the summer of the same year in Warsaw (the Polish capital).

The three countries each agreed to work on different aspects of codebreaking and the Poles promised to send two of their replica Enigma to France. Within a fortnight the Germans had launched their unprovoked attack on Poland, the event that was the *casus belli* for Britain and France to declare war on Germany.

Just prior to the start of the war one of those all important Enigma machines was brought to Britain and made its way to Bletchley Park.

This contribution was a real help, but still the key to the German codes had to be found, no easy task considering the fact that the Germans often changed them up to three times a day during the war.

Several leading Polish cryptanalysts made it to Britain, whilst others were captured by the Germans, tortured and killed – heroically never revealing what they knew.

Now the Enigma had to be solved and understood.

A Herculean task

On an average day in excess of 3,000 coded messages flooded in to Bletchley Park or *Station X* as it was often known. These messages were gathered by the 'Y' Stations. Once they arrived at BP they were then distributed to different huts for processing. Certain huts processed messages connected with the *Kriegsmarine* (German navy), others the *Wehrmacht* (German army) and the *Luftwaffe* (German air force).

After the Battle of Britain much of the attention was directed towards the activities of the German navy, especially its U-boats – these codes were sent to Hut 8.

It is important to understand what happened next.

Code breakers would spend hours comparing messages to see if they could identify patterns that would give a clue to how German commanders had set the rotor wheels of the Enigma – this was a painstaking and laborious task. It often helped that messages would begin with certain words; for vessels such as U-boats their messages invariably contained a brief weather report and this helped to give the code breakers a clue to how the rest of the message was encoded. These clues were known as a CRIB, once a CRIB was located it was tested out on an enormous machine called a *Bombe*. The *Bombe* was able to save time as it could process and check possible combinations far quicker than any person could. The Bombe would keep checking possible combinations and once it finished it meant that the code breakers CRIB had been right. Once the message was decoded it then had to be translated from German into English.

With the code cracked this meant that messages could be decoded until the next time the Germans changed the setting of the Enigma machine.

> **Fact -** Some codes were cracked within hours, other took many months.

Ultra

The activities at *Station X* required a range of specialists from mathematicians, deciphers, translators and those capable of evaluating the information and seeing how it could be put to effective use. All the information garnered was most secret, ultra-secret, hence why it was given the code name ULTRA. Only a few of people were allowed to receive ULTRA data, including Winston Churchil. At this stage the Germans had no idea that the British were able to break their codes, so ULTRA needed to be protected at all costs. ULTRA was not allowed to be mentioned and the British used a variety of tactics to draw attention away from their work. To prevent the Germans from suspecting that their codes had been intercepted and broken, the British and their allies occasionally took no action even when they were aware of enemy plans.

The Secret of ULTRA did not become public knowledge until 1974 – nearly thirty years after the end of the Second World War.

Fact - From 1942 the Americans were allowed access to ULTRA, but Soviet Russia wasn't as Winston Churchill never fully trusted Stalin and the Russians.

Some examples of how code breaking made a difference:

North Africa (1942)
By breaking codes used by Erwin Rommel's German forces, the British and British Empire forces could attack his supply routes, thus helping to ensure Bernard Montgomery's victory in the Second Battle of El Alamein in the Western Desert.

Battle of the Atlantic (1939 – 1944)
ULTRA was used to divert vessels away from the danger of the U-boat threat until convoys were better protected by escort ships and air cover.

D-Day (1944)
ULTRA revealed the location and size of German forces prior to the Normandy landings.

A legend of cryptanalysis

Just as Watson-Watt's name is forever to be associated with RADAR, the same is true of Alan Turing's when it comes to that of Bletchley Park.

Extraordinarily gifted individuals were thick on the ground at *Station X*, but one remarkable individual seemed to typify the brilliance of those who worked at Bletchley Park. Alan Turing (1912-1954) was a mathematician who relished wrestling with challenging problems. In the 1930s whilst exploring a complex problem connected to number theory, he invented the digital computer – this he called the "universal machine". So ahead of his time was his invention, that it would take another decade before one of these devices could be built. The Second World War interrupted his work and he soon found himself at Bletchley Park where he not only succeeded in developing a British bombe, developed from ideas brought by Enigma experts from Poland, he was also instrumental in cracking the code for the Enigma machine. Whilst at Bletchley he

Fact - There is a computer room at King's College, Cambridge named after Turing.

Visit: www.buckstv.co.uk and search for Bletchley Park

was head of Hut 8, the section that had particular responsibility for cracking the German naval codes. Later in 1942 he devised a new technique called *Turingismus* or *Turingery* to be used against the Lorenz cipher used by the Germans *Geheimschreiber* machine (secret writer) – this new German machine was codenamed 'Fish' by the British.

Alan Turing one of the many remarkable people who worked at *Station X*

A tightening grip

Whilst *Station X* did its work the Nazis tightened their grip on occupied Europe and were determined to starve Britain into surrender.

It would be very easy to think that once the Battle of Britain had been won Britain was safe, but this was not so. The Blitz of British cities continued and the German war machine sought to cripple Britain's war effort by waging war in the Atlantic whereby hundreds of thousands of tonnes of shipping was sunk. Many of these vessels were merchant ships bringing essential supplies from the British Empire or from the USA. Bletchley Park played an important part in intercepting coded U-boat messages and military commands that threatened Britain's very existence. The secret wireless war enabled the interception of wireless communications from the German Legation, Dublin. The Irish Republic (then called the Irish Free State) was neutral during the Second World War, but the British feared that the Republic would be used as a launch pad for the Germans to invade the rest of the British Isles. Communications were intercepted that indicated that some U-boats were re-fuelling in Western Ireland.

> **Fact -** For historical reasons many people in the Irish Republic were anti-British and thus pro-German throughout the war.

> "Newly declassified records show President Douglas Hyde offered condolences to Nazi Germany's representative in Dublin over the death of Hitler.
>
> Until now, historians had believed that the then Taoiseach Eamon de Valera was the only leader to convey official condolences to Eduard Hempel, director of the German diplomatic corps in Ireland.
>
> De Valera's gesture - unique among leaders of neutral nations in the final weeks of World War II."
>
> The Irish Independent, 31st December 2005

In mainland Europe the Nazis forbade listening to foreign radio broadcasts, especially the BBC.

Threat from beneath the waves

U-boats were a highly effective fighting force and yet it was one of them that was to yield a valuable treasure.

As an island nation Britain was particularly vulnerable to blockade. Then, as now, it did not grow sufficient foodstuffs to feed its entire population and so was heavily dependent on imports not just of food, but also of raw materials. The U-boat threat was a major one and the German submarines patrolled the North Atlantic and other seas and oceans in 'wolfpacks' hunting for Allied shipping. Each day the U-boat commanders communicated with the German Naval High Command by using their Enigma machines. Once the message was encrypted it was sent via wireless using Morse Code. The Germans were confident that the Enigma machine was invincible and that even if one was captured the Allies would not be able to crack the code.

In February 1941 the German trawler *Krebs* was captured off Norway, on board were two Enigma machines. Then in May 1941 the German weather vessel *München* was attacked and found to have a machine and part of the code books for June – on both occasions the crew had started to destroy the Enigma machines before their ships were captured by the Royal Navy.

On the evening of 8th May 1941 a British convoy was being stalked by two wolf pack submarines, U-110 and U-201. U-110 successfully launched two torpedoes, each hitting their targets the *Esmond* and the *Bengore.* A third torpedo went wide and a fourth stuck inside the tube. Water pumped in to discharge the torpedo failed to have the desired effect and unbalanced it severely limiting the submarine's options when its periscope was spotted by *HMS Aubretia.*

Definition: SIGNIT:- Signals intelligence – information gained from breaking ciphers and codes.

A miraculous catch

Soon both *HMS Aubretia* and *HMS Broadway* were above the German sub and were able to detect it by using asdic sonar equipment. Once detected they started laying down depth charges set for the depth detected. In the resulting explosions *U-110* was violently shaken, its batteries were damaged along with its port propeller, but most serious of all its emergency compressed air was leaking into the submarine. Without this the sub could not be controlled so its commander gave the order to surface.

Once on the surface *HMS Bulldog* was heading straight for the stricken sub, opening fire with a combination of Lewis and Pom Pom guns. The German Commander – Kapitänleutnant Fritz-Julius Lemp gave the order to "Abandon Ship" clearly believing that the vessel was about to be rammed and sunk with its precious secrets still on board. When cornered, U-boat captains scuttled their ships, rather than letting them fall into the hands of the allies.

The British ceased the attack and an armed boarding party was launched. *U-110* was captured, damaged but intact. History records that 15 Germans were killed or drowned during this encounter, they were the Captain, three Petty Officers and eleven naval ratings. The rest of the crew were taken prisoner and kept in a secure location so that the German Naval High Command would not hear about the capture of the *U-110*.

> **Fact -** *U-110* was the first of only three U-boats boarded and captured intact during the Second World War.

The Royal Navy had not only succeeded in capturing an Enigma machine, they had also discovered the code books containing the rotor settings for the machine – a real stroke of good fortune. The Enigma machine was immediately taken to Bletchley Park.

The tide begins to turn

Once at Bletchley, Alan Turing worked with a team of cryptographers and code breakers, and eventually broke the Enigma's cipher. This was to prove the turning point of the Battle of the Atlantic. Having broken the Enigma's cipher, the British were able to eavesdrop on all of the *Kriegsmarine's* communications to the U-boat fleet. It also finally convinced the Royal Navy that they needed to improve some of their own encryption as it became clear that the Germans themselves were successfully breaking some of the British code and cipher systems.

As early as 1935 *B-Dienst* had broken the most widely used British Naval code and by the early years of the war the Germans had broken into enough British Naval codes that the Germans knew the positions of all British warships (the Germans had also broken the American, Danish and Russian code systems).

Nazi Germany's decrypting operations were greatly hampered by the fact that it had a large number of cryptographic organisations which often failed to collaborate and so this sometimes resulted in duplication and a lack of knowledge sharing. Germany had also lost many of its greatest scientists as a result of its racist policies directed against the Jews.

Britain was soon in a position to call on the considerable resources and expertise of the Americans once the USA entered the war. Britain's enormous empire also meant that it could have listening stations dotted around the globe. In an age of Total War the ability to draw on intellectual and material resources and contacts was to be the difference between life and death.

Research:- For a wealth of other information about *U-110* and U-boats and the submarine war visit:

www.uboat.net/boats/u110.htm

www.uboatarchive.net

www.rnsubmus.co.uk

The Birth of a Colossus

By 1942 the war had entered a whole new phase, particularly after the Japanese attack on Pearl Harbor in December 1941.

With Britain and America now at war with Germany's ally Japan, the conflict was even more widespread. With increased activity in the Far East and the Pacific it meant yet more material flowing into *Station X*, also with America's entry into the war, a number of American personnel arrived at Bletchley to see what they could learn of its activities.

Knowledge sharing became essential, albeit in a rather guarded way. The relationship of Britain and the USA sharing sensitive data still continues to this very day.

Yet the Allies faced a real challenge - how to handle the vast amount of coded material flowing in to Bletchley. Naturally, the number of staff was steadily increased (by the end of the war nearly 10,000 people worked there).

In 1943 Tommy Flowers and a team of Post Office engineers at the Post Office Research Station in Dollis Hill developed **Colossus** an incredible code-breaking device that could process information four times faster than anything developed previously.

So what was Colossus like? It was a form of computer that was as large as a room, approximately 5 metres (16.4ft) in length, 3 metres (9.84ft) in width and 2.5 metres (8.2ft) high. It was capable of reading 5,000 letters of teleprinter tape a second! Later a Colossus Mark 2 was built and this was even faster.

Data being collected by the British Radio Security Service (The RSS) and its Voluntary Interceptors (VIs) was flooding in and had to be processed, decoded and evaluated.

The Great Delusion

Throughout the war various countries often mistakenly believed that their coding systems were unbreakable.

Overconfidence was to dog both the German and Japanese war efforts. Neither power had any understanding of the fact that their code systems had been broken. Both countries were highly organised and had formidable armed forces, yet they had underestimated the ingenuity of their opponents – a fatal error. The British Admiralty had made a similar error for a time and this had cost the British dear in terms of lost shipping and lives during the Battle of the Atlantic. With nations believing that their coded messages were unbreakable, this presented the opportunity to gain not just valuable data, but potentially to send bogus messages using the coding system. War by its very nature is about bluff and counter bluff, seeking to convince the enemy that something is there when it is not and that it isn't when it is. Great minds were employed in double-crossing the enemy and then seeing how well the enemy had been tricked by following their coded traffic.

Through the information decoded, it was possible to follow changes in troop and vehicle movements. There were innumerable occasions throughout the war where various theatrical elements were added to give credence to events. Two events worthy of further research are:

- Operation Mincemeat – 1943
- Operation Copperhead – 1944

It is important to remember that as well as information gathered from interceptions there were networks of spies and informants. All this makes it all the more remarkable that the Germans never found out about *Station X*. Churchill was a great admirer of the staff at Bletchley Park; *"They were the geese that laid the golden eggs and never cackled."* – their code of silence was to help maintain the deception.

The coming of the end

With Germany at war with Britain, the British Empire, the USA and Soviet Russia, it began to feel the strain. *Ultra* had allowed the Allies to access vital data and so target their resources more effectively. The great brains at *Station X*, such as Hugh Alexander (a British chess grand master), John Jeffreys, Dilly Knox, Alan Turing and Gordon Welchman had successfully cracked the Lorenz cipher and were aware of German V1 and V2 rockets at Peenemünde.

Bletchley Park suffered only minor bomb damage during the war and that was more by accident than design. Interestingly the important work on Radar had to move twice, firstly from Bawdsey Manor, Suffolk to Worth Matravers on the Isle of Purbeck, Dorset, then to Malvern, Worcestershire.

By the time the war had turned in the Allies favour, *Station X* was still shrouded in secrecy and by 1944 played a pivotal role in helping trick the Germans in believing that that the Allies were planning to land in the Pas de Calais and not Normandy. The story of the D-Day landings which began on 6th June 1944, might have been very different had not the Germans been hoodwinked by a complex and detailed operation of deception. Bletchley Park undoubtedly saved lives and in the opinion of many historians, contributed to the shortening of the war. It even helped gather significant information about the Nazi Holocaust against the Jews that was later able to be used at the Nuremberg War Trials.

Whilst the systems were not flawless they had played an important part in the downfall of Adolf Hitler and his hateful Nazi regime. With the war in Europe won, attention moved to operations in the east against the Japanese.

> **Fact -** The Germans didn't realise their codes had been cracked.

War in the East

As early as 1932 the Royal Netherlands Navy in Batavia in the Dutch East Indies (now Jakarta, Indonesia) had set up a radio interception unit to monitor the movements of the Japanese Navy.

The growing military might of Japan had troubled Britain and the USA and so they too monitored the situation with growing alarm. Following Pearl Harbor and the Fall of Singapore, Japan's activities were tracked from a whole range of locations, including:

- Wireless Experimental Centre, Delhi.
- Western Wireless Signal Centre, Bangalore.
- Eastern Wireless Signal Centre, near Calcutta.
- Indian Special Wireless Depot, Rawalpindi.
- American unit US8, Delhi.
- RAF 367 Wireless Unit, Cox's Bazaar.
- Station Anderson, Colombo.

Code breakers at Bletchley managed to gain access to the messages of General Hiroshi Oshima at the Japanese Embassy in Berlin. Soon from *Station X* to the Northern Territories in Australia the Japanese were being monitored and by the latter stages of the war, outwitted and ultimately defeated. Like their German allies they never believed that their codes such as the Kana code could ever being deciphered. In an age of Total War, in an era of a World War the techniques and strategies of the Secret Wireless War had proved decisive.

The technology of war was to take on a whole new dimension with the arrival of the

atomic bomb. War had proved an engine of incredible change, of scientific advancement and of almost unimaginable human suffering.

The dropping of two atomic bombs finally causes Japan to surrender.

Ingenuity and Inhumanity

In an age of Total War, history shows two different aspects of humankind; one is of darkness, death and destruction, the other of light, life and creativity. No one side has a monopoly of either. The Second World War is littered with such seeming absurdities as the Lowne's Works, Boone Street, Lee (South London) - manufacturing compasses disguised as buttons to the remarkable minds that shaped the destinies of the world by perfecting Radar technology or helping to crack fiendishly complicated codes and ciphers. The story of Radar and the Secret Wireless War is an extraordinary tale of the power of human ingenuity to endeavour to thwart and defeat those seeking to inflict their evil ideology on others.

The secret nature of much of this work means that many of those who worked so tirelessly may never be known. Some information may never be declassified and consequently there is every likelihood that we will only ever know part of the story.

History helps us gain an understanding of the past, and can equip us to question those who would seek to govern, monitor and 'control' us now and in the future.

The following words told to a group of new recruits joining the Australian Special Wireless Group during the Second World War, should make us all think about those who worked so tirelessly, yet may at times seem to have been totally forgotten:

"Not only do you not exist, you never will have existed. You will remain for always unknown and unacknowledged. There will be no awards, no glory. There will be no medals for this unit."

> **Fact -** The important work established at Bletchley moved to a new home at Cheltenham some years after the end of the war.

Glossary

Blitz – taken from the German word *Blitzkrieg* ('lightning war'), the Blitz became the word used to describe the German bombing of British cities which lasted from September 1940 until May 1941.

Blitzkrieg – German for 'lightning war'. A high speed military campaign using ground and air forces.

Cipher – a method of substituting letters or numbers for the letters of a message or of transforming their order.

Code – a system of substituting groups of two or more letters or numbers for the words, phrases or sentences of a message.

Codebreaker – a person who reconstructs enemy coded messages.

Cryptanalysis – the technique of breaking codes and ciphers.

Decipher – to transform a cipher signal into plain language.

Democracy – Government by the people or their elected representatives, as in Britain, Canada and the USA.

ENIGMA – the cipher machine used by the German military throughout the 1930s and during the Second World War.

GCHQ – British Government Communication Headquarters established at Bletchley Park, now based at Cheltenham. During the Second World War it had a series of code names: Station X, Mousetrap, War Station Room 47 and HMS Pembroke.

Nazi (National Socialist) Party – extreme political party led by Adolf Hitler which controlled Germany from 1933 – 1945.

Soviet Union – also known as the USSR (Union of Soviet Socialist Republics), which existed from 1922 – 1991; commonly known as Russia.

Squadron – a sub-group of an air force. In the RAF during the Second World War this normally meant sixteen aircraft at full strength.

Taoiseach – is the title taken by each Irish prime minister (in the Republic of Ireland)

Useful websites for Further Research:

Bletchley Park
www.bletchleypark.co.uk

British Inventors Society
www.thebis.org

Britain at War Experience
www.britainatwar.co.uk

Centre for Second World War Studies
www.secondworldwar.bham.ac.uk

Commonwealth War Graves Commission
www.cwgc.org

Defence Electronics History Society
www.dehs.org.uk

Defence Science & Technology Laboratory
www.dstl.gov.uk

Empire Museum
www.empiremuseum.co.uk

Espionage Information
www.espionageinfo.com

Imperial War Museum
www.iwm.org.uk

Kent Battle of Britain Museum
www.kbobm.org

MI5
www.mi5.gov.uk

National Archives
www.nationalarchives.gov.uk

National Army Museum
www.national-army-museum.ac.uk

National Memorial Arboretum
www.thenma.org.uk

Peace Pledge Union
www.ppu.org.uk

Purbeck Radar
www.purbeckradar.org.uk

Radar World
www.radarworld.org

RAF Museum
www.rafmuseum.org.uk

Royal Naval Museum
www.royalnavalmuseum.org

Secret Intelligence Service
www.sis.gov.uk

Second World War Experience Centre
www.war-experience.org

Second World War Northern Ireland
www.secondworldwarni.org

Bibliography

Arthur, Max. *Lost Voices of the Royal Air Force*, Hodder & Stoughton, London, 2005.

Bishop, Patrick. *Fighter Boys*, Harper Perennial, London, 2004.

Breurer, William B. *Deceptions of World War II*, John Wiley & Sons, New York, 2001.

Ciano's Diary, William Heinemann Ltd, London, 1947.

Collier, Richard. *Eagle Day*, Hodder & Stoughton, London, 1966.

Deighton, Len. *Battle of Britain*, Book Club Associates, London, 1980.

Franks, Norman. *Battle of Britain*, Bison Books Ltd, London, 1982.

Gaskin, M.J. *Blitz*, Faber and Faber, London, 2005.

Glancey, Jonathan. *Spitfire*, Atlantic Books, London, 2006.

Hilton, Richard. *Nine Lives*, Hollis & Carter,

London, 1955.

Jackson, Ashley. *The British Empire and the Second World War*, Hambledon Continuum, London, 2006.

Lyttelton, Oliver. *The Memoirs of Lord Chandos*, The Bodley Head, London, 1962.

Mallman Showell, Jak P. *German Naval Codebreakers*, Naval Institute Press, Annapolis, 2003.

Neillands, Robin. *The Battle of Normandy 1944*, Cassell Military Paperbacks, London, 2003.

Overy, Richard. *The Dictators*, Allen Lane, London, 2004.

Preston, Paul. *A Concise History of the Spanish Civil War*, Fontana Press, 1996.

Smith, Michael. *New Cloak, Old Dagger*, Victor Gollancz, London, 1996.

Smith, Michael. *Station X*, Channel 4 Books, London, 1998.

Stripp, Alan. *Code Breaker in the Far East*, Oxford University Press, Oxford, 1995.

Wires, Richard. *The Cicero Spy Affair*, Praeger Publishers, Westport, Conneticut, 1999.

Acknowledgements

Maps:
Copyright TLWP Limited

Photographs:
Bundesarchiv
Francois Prins Collection
Hulton-Deutsch Collection / CORBIS
National Archives

Mark T Jones is an experienced writer, who has taught history for many years. He is a fervent internationalist, who has travelled widely. After time spent in Sierra Leone he wrote *Sierra Leone Reflections* and has recently been working on a film script for a film set during the Second World War.

Books

Available individually or as a commemorative pack:

    Flying For Freedom – A Pilot's Story

The Battle of Britain –
    A Definitive Chronology of Events

The Battle of Britain – A Timeline of Events

Aircraft of the Battle of Britain

Battlefield Britain

Opposing Genius

Pilots of the Battle of Britain

Radar and the Secret Wireless War

Spitfire Pilot

Available individually or as a twin-set:

Allied Fighter Aces of World War 2

American Pilots of the Battle of Britain

Limited Edition Artwork

Spitfires 'Line-A-Stern'

'In – Readiness' (Spitfire on Airstrip)

'Into the Battlezone'

The Legendary 109

Hurricane!

Their Finest Hour Artwork 3D

Their Finest Hour 'Aircraft of the Battle of Britain' Postcards

DVDs

Battlefield Britain	2 x 90 minutes
Aircraft of the Battle of Britain	3 x 60 minutes
Opposing Genius	1 x 60 minutes
Pilots of the Battle of Britain	1 x 75 minutes
The Civilian War	1 x 60 minutes
Britain Stands Alone	3 x 60 minutes
Spitfire!	1 x 60 minutes

Limited Edition 'Spitfire' Smart Cars

Yes, 10 'Their Finest Hour' officially branded new smart cars. Personalised to incorporate the initials of purchaser. (Finance available, subject to status)

Music CDs

The 1940s Collection: 3 CDs brought together as a musical tribute to the era in one pack:

Dame Vera Lynn's 'White Cliffs of Dover'

Dorothy Lamour's 'Thanks for the Memory'

Glenn Miller's Moonlight Serenade

A4 and A5 Aicraft Illustrations

(Available individually or as a set of 12)
Supermarine Spitfire Mark 1, Hawker Hurricane Mark 1, Boulton Paul Defiant , Gloster Gladiator, Fairey Fulmar, Bristol Blenheim, Messerschmitt Bf 109E, Messerschmitt Bf 110C, Heinkel He 111 Bomber, Junkers Ju 87 'Stuka' Dive Bomber,, Junkers Ju 88 Bomber, Dornier Do 17 Bomber

Die Cast Models (1/72 Scale)

Supermarine Spitfire, Hawker Hurricane, Junkers Ju 87 'Stuka' Dive Bomber, Messerschmitt Bf 109

Plastic Models

Messerschmitt Bf 109E	1/24, 1/48, 1/72 scale
Junkers Ju 87-B 'Stuka'	1/24, 1/48, 1/72 scale
Supermarine Spitfire Mk 1	1/24, 1/48, 1/72 scale
Hawker Hurricane:	1/24, 1/72 scale

Other models 1/72 Scale

Heinkel He 111 Bomber, Junkers Ju 88 Bomber, Messerschmitt Bf 110-C, Gloster Gladiator, Boulton Paul Defiant, Fairey Fulmar (FAA), Bristol Blenheim, Dornier Do 17

Sets in 1/72 Scale

Battle of Britain Airfield Set, Luftwaffe Airfield Set, RAF Airfield Set
'Dogfight Double' - Junkers Ju 88 and Hawker Hurricane

Battle of Britain 70th Anniversary Set - Heinkel He 111 Bomber, Hawker Hurricane, Supermarine Spitfire and Messerschmitt Bf 109
Battle of Britain Commemorative Set - Supermarine Spitfire, Hawker Hurricane, Junkers Ju 87 'Stuka' Dive Bomber and Heinkel He 111 Bomber

Memorabilia and Coasters

1940s coins, stamps and other items, plus Battle of Britain Coasters and original pieces of memorabilia

**All 'TFH' products available
from the TFH official Website.
Subject to Availability.**

**www.theirfinesthour.co.uk or email:
products@theirfinesthour.co.uk**